"Hello, everyone! My name is Stardust and this is my little brother, Vincent. Together we are exploring some of the most amazing things about life on Earth."

"Stardust, where did plants and
animals come from? Was it magic?"

"No, Vincent, it wasn't magic.
But the process is even more special than magic!"

"We know some things about how life began on Earth, and we are still learning so many amazing details. One thing we know is that the earliest life on Earth consisted of single-celled organisms, somewhat like bacteria, which still exist."

"Those single-celled organisms gradually evolved into all life on Earth today—including YOU! Because of this, all forms of life on Earth are related to each other."

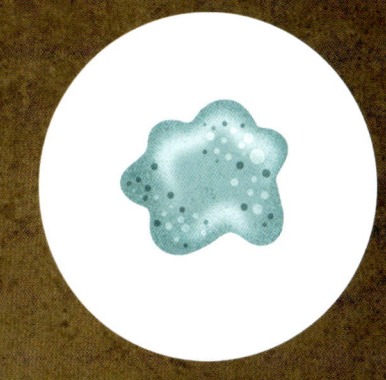

"Stardust, so I am related to trees and squirrels and fish?"

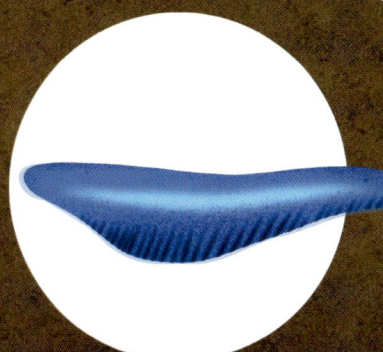

"Vincent, yes you are! Everything we know from genes, molecules, anatomy, fossils and other evidence shows that all forms of life on Earth are related to each other."

"Wow, Stardust! But that seems a little strange."

"It can be hard to understand at first. But as we explore the evidence for this on Earth, we see that we are all related. It is one of the most beautiful facts of life."

direct ancestors

cousins

"Vincent, we have two kinds of relatives. One kind are direct ancestors, like our parents and grandparents. And to them, we are their direct descendants—children and grandchildren. The single-celled organisms, ancient fish and early primates that directly evolved into humans are kind of like grandparents and great-grandparents to us.

The second kind of relatives are our cousins, who are not our ancestors or our descendants, but who share common ancestors in the past with us. Cousins may be living in the present or in the past. For example, living apes and monkeys are not the ancestors of humans, but they are our cousins. We are also cousins of cats and birds and oak trees and everything else. We are related to them, but we are not descended from any of them alive today."

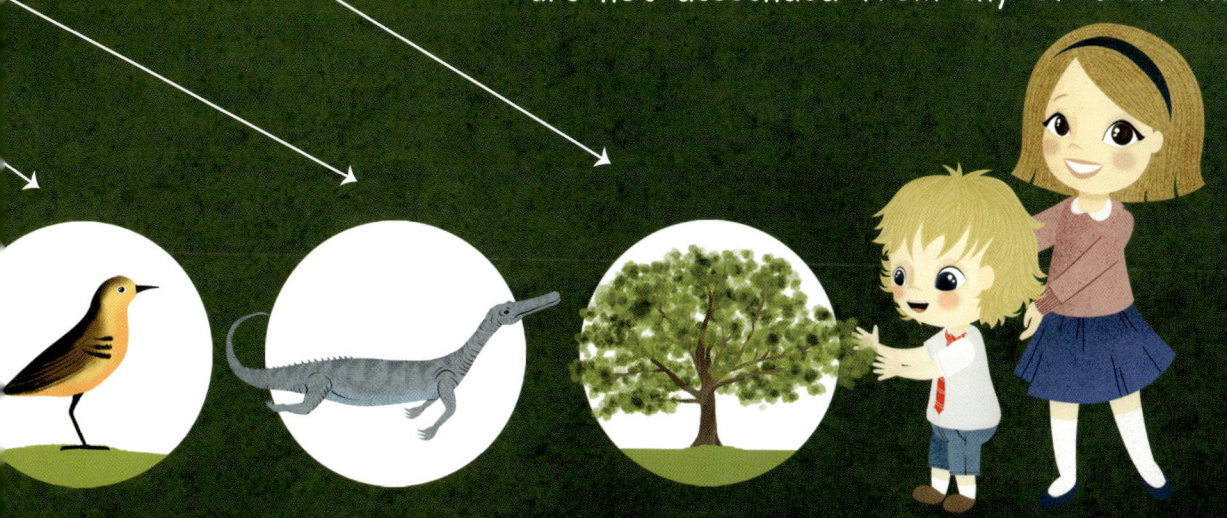

"Stardust, did all plants and animals come from the same ancestors?"

"Yes. Millions of years after Earth formed, life began with the simple, single-celled organisms that are the ancient ancestors of all living things on the planet today."

"So there were no people back then?"

"No, Vincent, there were not and the world looked very different from how it looks now!"

"There was almost no oxygen in the air. There were no trees or flowers. There were no humans. There were no birds in the sky, no fish in the water or any other kinds of animals. For the first three billion years after life began on Earth, the only life forms were simple, single-celled organisms much like bacteria still surviving today."

"Earth has changed in many ways since it formed, and it is still changing today. For example, the continents, the land that we see today, have been moving and changing shape over hundreds of millions of years.

The continents are part of the hard outer layer of the Earth, called the crust. Because a layer beneath is made of molten rock and metal that are semi-liquid, the continents move very slowly, almost like leaves on top of a pond.

This is what Earth looked like 225 million years ago. Scientists call that big continent Pangea. Since then, the continents have gradually separated and moved to where they are located today."

"Good question, Vincent. We can see this by looking at the shapes of the continents today. See, they fit together like a puzzle to form the bottom half of Pangea.

We can also see this by looking at the fossil remains of plants and animals that lived together on Pangea before the continents separated. For example, there was an animal that lived on Pangea called *Lystrosaurus* and we can see its fossil remains on three different continents today—Africa, India and Antarctica. *Lystrosaurus* couldn't swim across the oceans, so this shows us that these three continents were once connected."

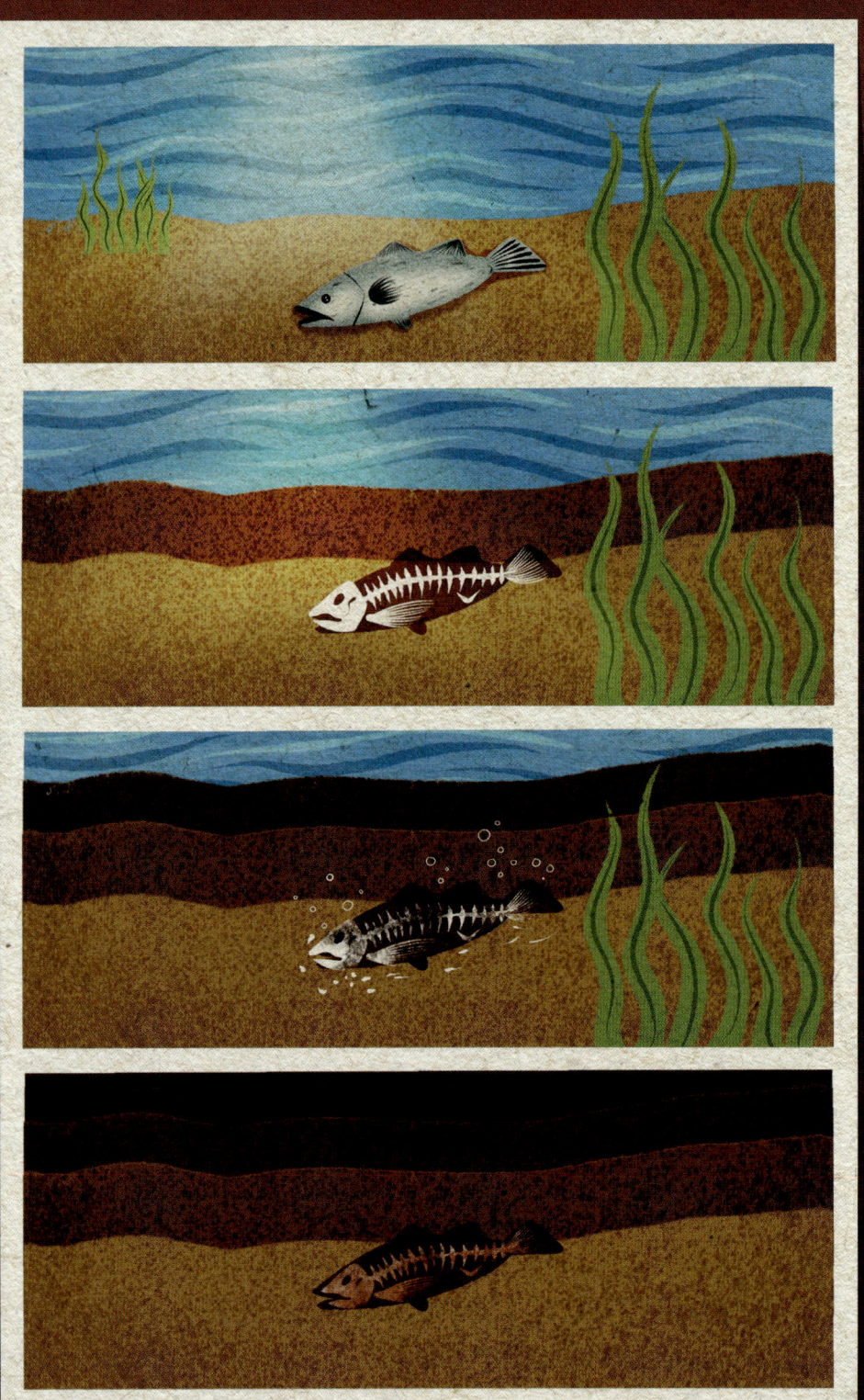

"Stardust, What are fossils?"

"Fossils are the remains of once-living things that are preserved in rock. Fossils can come from lots of things, like the bones or teeth of an animal, wood from a tree or even whole insects. Fossils can also be traces that a living thing leaves behind, like footprints or even poop! Scientists have a name for fossil poop. It's called a coprolite.

Because new layers of rock form on top of older layers, fossils can help us understand how long ago those plants and animals lived and which ones came first."

"Stardust, how do fossils help us know that?"

"Vincent, as we dig our way through Earth or look at layers of rock on the surface to learn about our planet's history, fossils can help us see what life looked like in the past and how we are related to all other animals, fungi and plants.

In the most recent layers of Earth's history, which were formed during what geologists call the Cenozoic Era (66 million years ago through today), we find the fossil remains of modern-looking mammals. This includes our early human ancestors, such as 'Lucy,' who lived 3.2 million years ago in Africa.

As we dig even deeper into Earth's history, we find the Mesozoic Era (252 million to 66 million years ago). This is where we see the first fossil remains of mammals and dinosaurs.

Below this, in the early Paleozoic Era (540 million to 252 million years ago), we see an explosion of life on Earth. As we dig into these layers of Earth, we find fossils of plants and animals including coral, insects, ferns, fish and amphibians."

"Stardust, how many different kinds of animals are there?"

"Today, we have more than a million different species of animals on Earth! All of them, including us, come from ancestors that have lived on Earth in the past."

Miacid

"Often, one animal evolves over time into many different animals. The miacids were a good example of this. Miacids were a group of ancient carnivores that evolved into many modern animals including lions, foxes, dogs, bears and raccoons.

These animals are our cousins. They evolved into different animals because of many tiny changes that happened over 30 million years, while they were living in different places on Earth. These changes helped them live longer and have more babies."

"Stardust, have any other animals evolved like that?"

"Yes! There are thousands of fun examples of this.

Here is my favorite example: A group of brown bears migrated north to the Arctic around 500,000 years ago. A small mutation created white fur in one of the bears and this bear then had babies with white fur. The bears with white fur were able to blend in with the snow and ice and were able to sneak up on other animals. They were better hunters so they had more food to eat. Because of this, they lived longer and had more babies. The descendants of those white bears are what we call polar bears today."

"Stardust, what is your favorite animal?
Mine are bears because of my favorite stuffed animal, Mr. Bear."

"Vincent, the dog is this girl's best friend.
Did you know that dogs are the direct descendants of wolves?"

"Really? Some dogs look a little like wolves, but a lot of dogs don't look like wolves at all! How did that happen?"

"Well, Vincent, wolves started living with humans thousands of years ago. After a while, the wolves that lived with humans were separated from the other wolves for long enough that they began to evolve into a different animal—the dog.

But this doesn't mean that all wolves have become dogs. The wolf is still on Earth today. The wolves that lived with humans simply had so many small changes over thousands of years that they are becoming a different species. The process is not complete yet, but we can observe it happening."

"Over the past few centuries, humans have helped create hundreds of different types of dogs. By selecting for dogs with features that we like, such as nose size, color, height or behaviors, we are able to help change dogs over time to look and act like we want. We now have hundreds of different dog breeds."

"Because humans were involved, these changes happened much faster than they would have in nature. It's hard to believe, but both Chihuahuas and Great Danes evolved from wolves and are the same species!

My dog, Lady, is a King Charles Spaniel. This type of dog was bred to be fun, playful and gentle with a long, silky coat. It also loves to cuddle, which I love about my Lady."

"Wow! That is so cool, Stardust!
What other animals have evolved like the wolf?"

"There are so many fun examples of this! Did you know that the ancestor of whales had legs and walked on land?"

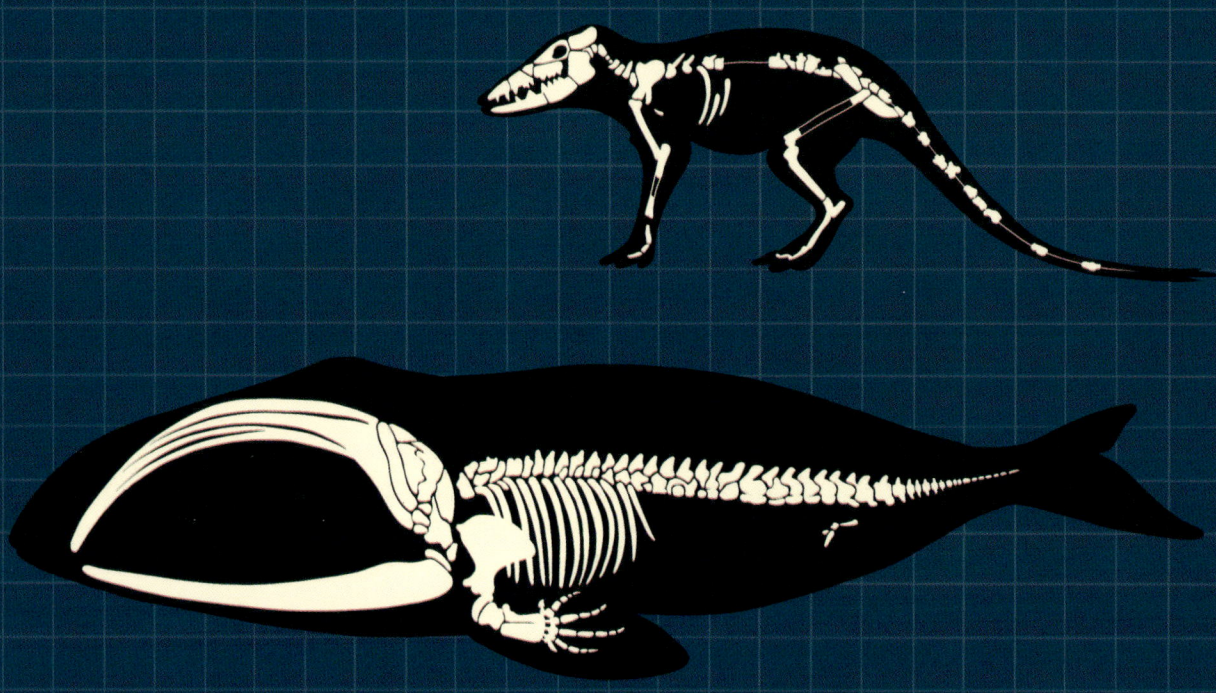

"No, I thought that they were a kind of fish because they swim in the ocean."

"Whales are mammals just like you and me, Vincent! They are warm-blooded, feed their babies with milk, breathe air with their lungs and many of them have hair."

"Fossil animals called *Pakicetus* lived 50 million years ago and are known as the 'first whales.' The *Pakicetus* were mammals that lived on land and in the sea. They ate meat, including fish. We think these early whale ancestors moved into the water to help them survive better. Over millions of years, their children and children's children evolved to become good swimmers, to have fins, flippers, and flukes and to never return to land.

Many whales still have hip bones inside their bodies that were used when their ancestors walked on land and still had hind limbs. And they have hand bones, just like we do, inside of their front flippers!

Compare these pictures, Vincent, of the arm and hand bones of a whale, on the left, and of a human, on the right."

"Stardust, it's so exciting to know how I'm connected to all life on Earth!"

"I agree, little brother. I love to learn about our connection to everything on Earth. This helps me appreciate how special we are to be living creatures that learn and grow on this beautiful planet that is spinning through space—all made of stardust!"

Glossary

Amphibian: a small, cold-blooded animal that usually spends part of its life cycle in water and part of its life cycle on land. Examples include frogs and salamanders.

Anatomy: the study of the structure of living things.

Ancestor: a person or group who lived in the past and from whom later lineages are descended.

Arctic: the polar region located at the northernmost part of Earth.

Bacteria: a kind of microscopic single-celled organism. Bacteria are among the simplest creatures that are considered alive. For example, *E. coli* is a common species which lives in the human gut.

Carnivore: an animal that gets the majority of its food from eating other animals.

Continent: one of the large, continuous land masses on Earth. Seven are commonly recognized today, but the number has varied over very long geological time periods.

Descendant: a person or group whose origin derives from a particular ancestor in the past.

Evolve: when a group of living things changes over time and can pass these changes down to the next generation.

Evidence: something that gives proof or reason to accept an idea.

Extinct: a species that no longer exists in living form.

Fossil: the preserved remains or traces of an ancient animal or plant.

Fungus: a member of the group of living things, neither plant nor animal, which includes mushrooms, molds, yeasts, and truffles.

Gene: the basic unit of heredity that exists inside the cells that make up living things.

Geologist: a scientist who studies the composition and history of the Earth.

Magic: a supernatural power that is used to make impossible things happen.

Mammal: an animal that is warm-blooded, has fur or hair, has a skeleton inside its body, and feeds its young with milk produced by the mother.

Molecule: the smallest unit of a substance that has all the properties of that substance.

Organism: an individual living thing, such as a plant, animal, or bacterium.

Primates: the group of mammals that includes humans, monkeys, and apes.

Species: a group of organisms which are part of an ancestral-descendant lineage formed by reproduction.

About the Author

Thirteen-year-old Bailey Harris is an author, speaker and advocate for freethought and human rights. She is the author of the *Stardust* series of science books for young readers. Bailey is on a mission to inspire a love of science and a sense of wonder about the universe, promote freethought, and work towards acceptance of scientific fact in society and government. She was eight years old when she was inspired to write her first book, a beautifully illustrated children's book that presented sound science in a manner accessible to young readers and pre-readers.

Learn more at stardustscience.com

"Where did life come from and how did it get so diverse? The ancient Greeks asked these questions, but it took 2,500 years for scientists to figure it out. The answer isn't difficult but it is counterintuitive, which is why children must explore these questions as early as possible so that their consciousness is raised to accept the fact of evolution. The way Stardust explains evolution to little Vincent warms my Darwinian heart, especially since Vincent has half my DNA! I love this book and will give a copy to every kid and parent I know."

—Michael Shermer, Publisher Skeptic magazine, columnist Scientific American, author of *Heavens on Earth*

"Stardust authors, Bailey and Douglas Harris, take a thoughtful approach to evolution's potential for controversy. As a result, their evidence-based and wonder-filled book can be enjoyed by families of faith and non-faith backgrounds. The story's heart is a sister who can't wait to tell her little brother about how science shows we are all related! She weaves together rigorous yet relatable research to amaze us with life's unity and diversity. On every page, readers will share in the siblings' curiosity — a human trait found like stardust everywhere."

— Ariel Marcy, Founder STEAM Galaxy Studios, Fulbright Scholar (evolutionary biology), game designer of Go Extinct!